CHRISTMAS CA
FOR
FINGERSTYLE GUITAR

By Doug Young

www.dougyoungguitar.com

ISBN 978-0-9896349-4-6

To download audio recordings, visit
http://bit.ly/FingerstyleChristmas

ACKNOWLEDGEMENTS

Thanks to:

Teri Young for editing and
supporting this project.

Cover photo:

Ed Claxton EM model guitar

TABLE OF CONTENTS

FORWARD

As with other books in this series, the arrangements in this book are meant to be easy to play, easy to read, and most of all, easy to extend. There are two basic approaches to playing fingerstyle arrangements: memorize every note of an intricate piece and play it the same way every time, or start with an outline of the tune, and improvise variations. The first approach has the advantage that the notes are worked out ahead of time, but takes work to memorize. The music may also get stale over time, since everything is locked in. With the second approach, memorization is easier (or maybe even unnecessary), and you can continually explore new variations, making the music more fun to play, and maybe more fun to listen to.

Christmas tunes are ideally suited for the improvisational approach. Most musicians don't perform them all year long, and it's challenging to maintain a repertoire of memorized arrangements that get played only during the holidays. The arrangements in this book are designed to be pulled out at a moment's notice, allowing you to perform seasonal music with minimal preparation. These sketches are similar to those found in "fake books," but designed for solo fingerstyle guitar. Jazz fake books are typically limited to just chord names and perhaps melody. These arrangements provide a bit more than that – basically easy-to-play arrangements with no complicated parts that are designed to be extended on the fly.

These were my goals:

1.   The arrangements must be in standard tuning to avoid retuning during a performance.

2.   The arrangements must be simple enough to read during the performance with minimal preparation and no memorization.

3.   No page turning required.

4.   The music should fall comfortably in first position, with simple fingerings.

5.   The songs must be in guitar-friendly keys. If you need to play in other keys for a singer or to match another instrument, consider using a capo.

6.   The arrangements should be as minimalist as possible, but lend themselves to simple embellishments during performance. We'll discuss this in more detail in the section on "How to Use This Book" on page 6.

7.   Each arrangement, although simple, should sound musical when played exactly as written. I often try to leverage simple re-harmonization to complement and enrich the song when played as a solo instrumental, without straying from the simple and recognizable character of the song.

I hope you find these arrangements useful for your own needs, whether you play them exactly as written, or take them as a starting point for your own enhanced arrangements.

Doug Young

ABOUT THE RECORDINGS

Audio recordings of the songs in this book can be downloaded from:

http://bit.ly/FingerstyleChristmas

For these recordings, I generally followed the approaches outlined on page 9. I played each tune the first time exactly as written, so you can follow along and hear how the arrangement is supposed to sound if you just follow the music exactly. Then I continued with one or two additional verses, improvising embellishments. In many cases, I also improvised introductions or endings for the songs.

The improvised sections are not written out – that would defeat the entire goal of the book. I elaborated on the written arrangement on the fly during recording, and probably would not (or could not) play the song exactly the same way again. However, I briefly describe how I approached each song in the notes on the page before each song. I encourage you to explore your own ideas, not necessarily to work out the embellishments I added.

Where I thought it might be useful or instructive, I have written out some of my improvised introductions or endings in the notes before each song. These segments provide some examples of techniques that can be used to add some interest to the songs. But again, I'd just take these as seeds for your own ideas!

HOW TO USE THIS BOOK

The arrangements in this book can be used in several ways. They can be played exactly as written, either as solo instrumentals, or to accompany singers. They can also be used as the basis of your own interpretations, which you can either work out in advance, or "improvise" variations on the fly. By improvise, in this context, I don't mean playing guitar solos like you would in jazz or rock music; I mean simply taking liberties with the arrangement, adding embellishments and variations on what is written.

Let's briefly explore each of these scenarios: playing as written, backing up singers, and embellishing the songs to create longer arrangements. We'll also touch on adding introductions and endings.

Playing Instrumentally As Written

I've designed these arrangements to be fairly easy to play – as easy as I could make them while still sounding musical. The music is written in two staffs with both standard notation and tablature – a fairly common convention these days. The chord names and shapes are also provided above the staff. The chord shapes shown often indicate a subset of the full chord, reflecting the fingering being used in the arrangement at that point.

Each arrangement consists of only a single pass through the song, which will be quite short, in most cases. You can repeat the song as many times as you like. In songs that have pickup notes, I have followed a non-conventional notation technique of showing the pickup notes in the last measure in parenthesis. This is meant to indicate that you can play them when repeating the tune, but skip them on the final time through. Usually this would be shown as first and second endings, but that creates more complex-looking notation, and I wanted to avoid any distraction or complexity as much as possible.

The interpretation of these songs is entirely up to you. If you use these arrangements to accompany others, it's often best to keep things simple, and above all, keep a steady tempo. When performing instrumentally, you can play with more feeling and expression, playing slower, or even varying the tempo or playing more rubato.

Supporting Singers

These arrangements should work well as a way to support singers, either for a performance or as a sing-along. You could play the music as written, which is usually most effective when supporting a group singing. If you are supporting a smaller group performance, you might decide to skip playing the melody, and rely primarily on the chord changes as a way to accompany the others.

In churches I have attended, pianists or organists usually started songs by playing the last phrase as an introduction, establishing the tempo – and also reminding the congregation of the song. If you want to use this approach, either to support singers, or even as an introduction for an instrumental version, I have marked the start of the last phrase with a ✱ symbol. This identifies the last phrase, which could be used as an introduction before playing the song from the beginning. For example, here are the final five measures of *Away in a Manger*:

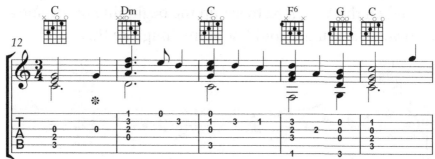

You could start the introduction with the last note of measure 12 and then play to the end.

In many cases, it would make sense to have the introduction end on the V or V7 chord (D or D7 in the key of G, G or G7 in the key of C, and so on). This isn't indicated in the arrangement, but is always an option you can introduce on your own. For example, you could play an introduction of *Away in a Manger* as follows (again, starting from the ✱):

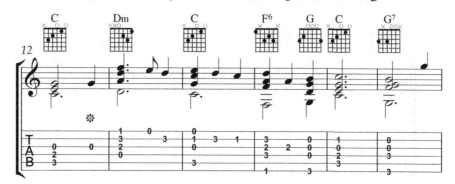

If you are performing with others and have time to rehearse, you might consider creating a less cookie-cutter introduction. Introductions can be as simple as playing arpeggios in the appropriate time signature and tempo over the first chord. For example, for *Away in a Manger*, you could playing something like this (the G at the end of the final measure is the pickup note into the melody):

Many common chord progressions within the key can be used as introductions. You can simply play a pattern using the right tempo and time signature to set up the tune. Here are a few ideas:

- I-V7 (C-G7 in the key of C). Play the I chord as long as seems appropriate – perhaps three measures – then end on the V7 chord to set up the beginning of the song. For example, an introduction to *Away In a Manger* could be something like this:

- Play I-IV-I-V7 (C, F, C, G7 in the key of C). This is just a variation of the above idea, but in this case, we're adding the IV chord for some extra color. For example, here's another possible introduction to *Away In a Manger*:

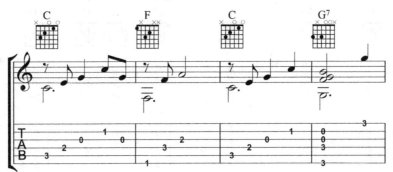

- Play I-vi-ii-V (C, Am, Dm, G7 in the key of C). This is a common chord progression in popular music and sounds a bit more sophisticated that the simple I-IV-V7 chords. Using this approach, you could create this introduction to *Away In a Manger*:

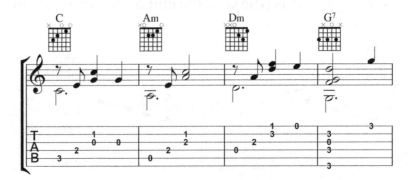

These are just a few ideas; feel free to explore and create your own introductions.

Playing Instrumentally With Variations

I primarily use these songs as solo fingerstyle instrumentals, which is how they are performed in the accompanying sample recordings. When performing solo, you have a lot of flexibility in how you interpret the songs. You can pick the tempo and add your own stylistic elements.

These arrangements should be simple enough that you can easily add arpeggios, passing notes, additional bass notes and so on, as you see fit, even when you are basically sight-reading the songs.

Here's what I typically do to turn these simple arrangements into full performances:

1. Add an introduction (see the discussion above about accompanying singers for some introduction ideas).

2. Play the song as written the first time through. I keep it as simple as possible. The most important thing in most situations is to not make distracting mistakes, people know these songs and will enjoy them even if – or maybe even especially if – they are played in a simple way that makes the melody clear. Played expressively, these arrangements should sound good exactly as written.

3. On the second time through the song, I start to add some arpeggios and extra chord notes in any spots where there is space. I don't want to obscure the melody, (and it is important to know the melody!), but some simple natural additions will make it sound like a more sophisticated arrangement. Less is more in most cases; it doesn't take a lot to enhance the song.

4. Having played two times through, if I am feeling confident of the song, I will take more liberties on a third pass. One approach is to vary the timing of the melody slightly – think of how a good singer might perform the song. I may slightly anticipate melody notes, and may also delay bass notes.

5. Finally, when I have played long enough, I add an ending. Endings can be as simple as slowing down – a ritard – on the final phrase. Or I might play a simple chord progression, like I-IV-I at the end. So if the song ends on a G, I'd play G, C, G. Another approach is to use a "tag" ending, where you repeat the final phrase. To do this effectively, you might slightly ritard as you approach the final measure, then go back the point indicated by a ✳ in the music (usually four bars from the end), and play that phrase again, with a more dramatic ritard on the closing measure.

More specific ideas for each song are included in the notes on the page before the song, but these are always just suggestions. Use your own ideas to extend or embellish the songs in any way that sounds good to you!

Let's look at a few ideas for introducing variations, using the first line of *Away In a Manger* (page 20) as an example.

The following example demonstrates adding some simple arpeggios as additional accompaniment. As long as you finger more or less complete chord shapes while playing the tune, you should be able to easily add these accompaniment patterns in many places. The key is to look for places where there is space, and to never forget to bring out the melody. Notice the delayed bass note on the F chord in measure 3. This is another way to vary the accompaniment and make the arrangement sound more complex and interesting.

In the following example, I'm taking some liberties with timing, slightly anticipating the initial melody note in each measure. This example also adds some additional bass notes, but keeps the accompaniment simpler than the previous example, because the intent of this technique is to emphasize the melody and give it a more vocal-like quality.

Here's another approach, using more or less continuous eighth-note arpeggios, weaving the melody notes in with the accompaniment. The more you add, the more important it becomes to make the melody notes stand out clearly, in contrast to the accompaniment.

Creating Endings

Let's look at a few ways to add endings, using *Away In a Manger* as an example. In this first example, the ending is signaled by simply slowing down in the final two measures, doubling the time of the last three melody notes and chords.

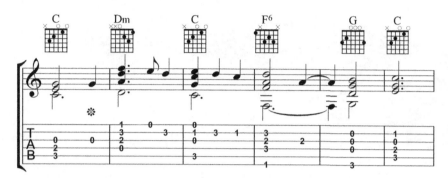

Moving from the final chord to the IV chord and back to the I is another approach. Here, we play a simple arpeggio pattern over C, then F, then back to a final C chord.

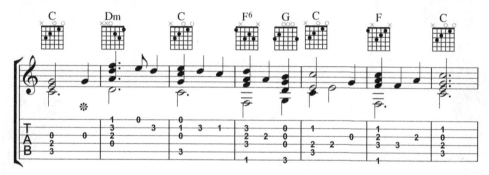

As a final example, lets look at one way to create a "tag" ending. Here, we play the last phrase, but substitute an Am for the final C, and then return to the final phrase (marked with a ❋), and play through to the end.

SONGS BY KEY

ANGELS WE HAVE HEARD ON HIGH

Words and Music: Traditional

Angels we have heard on high,
sweetly singing o'er the plains,
and the mountains in reply
echo back their joyous strains.

Angels We Have Heard on High is an English translation of an older French traditional song, *Les Anges dans nos campagnes*. James Chadwick loosely translated the original in 1862. The melody is another traditional French tune, *Gloria*.

Performance Tips and Comments

This arrangement is based entirely on fairly simple first position chords. It should not present many challenges, other than the chords changing every two beats.

Although I show mostly full fingerings in the chord diagrams, you don't necessarily need to finger the entire chord in most cases. For example, the opening G chord really only needs the 6th string bass note. Fingering the whole chord allows you to improvise a little more freely without fear of hitting a note that doesn't fit, but may make it more difficult to change chords smoothly. The Em7 in measure 2 is another example. I don't actually finger the 5th string, which makes the chord simpler, and since I'm playing fingerstyle, I can avoid hitting the 5th string. These comments generally apply to every song in this book. Experiment with what works for you.

The chord diagrams are more a guide to what I'm thinking as I play the chord, not necessarily the exact notes being played. In general, melody is the most important part, with the bass notes coming next. Everything else is "nice to have", but not required.

Introduction Suggestions

This tune is in 4/4 time, in the key of G, so any simple 4/4 chord pattern in G could work as an introduction. You could just play a few measures of G, or something like G, C, G, D7 to set up the tune. The final phrase, the last 3 measures, could also make good introduction.

Ending Suggestions

The last 3 measures (marked with a star) could be repeated for a "tag" ending. You could repeat measures 19 and 20 several times before finally resolving to the G in the last measure. You could also simply ritard into the final chord.

Sample Recording

On the sample recording, I played an introduction based on the opening chords of the verse – just arpeggios over G, a descending F# bass note, then Em. After playing the arrangement as written, I played additional chord tones and arpeggiated notes between the melody. I tried to keep my added notes below the melody to make sure they sound like accompaniment and don't obscure the melody. The chorus, starting at measure 9, has long half notes that provide a bit of space to fill. Some versions of this song will show a counter-melody in these sections, but rather than include that explicitly, it's simple to just arpeggiate those chords to simulate the effect. I'm simply playing a picking pattern of 8th notes over the G chord in measure 9, Am in measure 10, and so on.

For the ending, I repeated measures 19 and 20. Instead of ending on the final G chord the first time, I just jumped back to the G chord in measure 19 and repeated the phrase before ending.

ANGELS WE HAVE HEARD ON HIGH

Traditional
Arr. Doug Young

AULD LANG SYNE

Words: Robert Burns (1788)
Music: Traditional

Should old acquaintance be forgot,
and never brought to mind?
Should old acquaintance be forgot,
and auld lang syne?

While not technically a Christmas tune, *Auld Lang Syne* is typically sung around New Years, at the tail end of the Christmas season. The song is a poem, written by the Scottish poet Robert Burns. The melody comes from an older Scottish folk melody.

Performance Tips and Comments

This song fits comfortably in first position in the key of A. Although there are multiple verses, the song is usually only sung as a single verse and chorus. But as an instrumental, you can of course extend it however you like. The E9 chord in measure 8 and also the Bm chord in measure 12 could be skipped - just play the melody note if it too hard to grab the whole chord. You might also prefer the sound of an E9 as used in measure 8 instead of the Bm in measure 12. But the chord adds a nice emphasis to those pickup notes, and can be held out longer than written, if you like.

Introduction Suggestions

You could set up the song with the last 4, or even just the final 2 measures. Any picking pattern over A or A to E7 would also work well.

Ending Suggestions

Dramatically slowing down into the final phrase fits the way the song is often sung. The last line, starting with the pickup notes to measure 13 could also be repeated.

Sample Recording

For the example recording, I created an introduction by playing A to E twice. After the first time through, I played just the chords of the first 8 bars (the verse), as if I was accompanying a singer, creating a sort of interlude. This is a technique you could use to extend any song. Then I played the entire song a final time.

For the ending, I repeated the last four bars, starting with the pickup note to measure 13, playing more slowly on the repeat. I also introduced an F diminished chord in measure 14. You could think of this as just raising the root of the E chord up to an F, while keeping the other notes of the chord (G# and B) the same. Here's what I played for the final four bars:

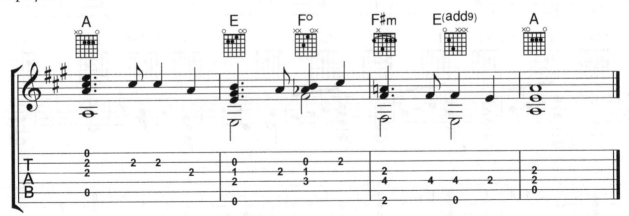

AULD LANG SYNE

Robert Burns
Arr. Doug Young

AWAY IN A MANGER (MUELLER)

Words: Unknown/Traditional
Music: James Murray (1887)

Away in a manger
No crib for His bed
The little Lord Jesus
Laid down His sweet head.

Away in a Manger's origins are a bit murky. The lyrics are often attributed to Martin Luther, but there is no evidence he actually wrote it. There are two popular melodies used for the song. This one was first published in 1887 by James Murray (who attributed the lyrics to Luther). Mysteriously, by 1914, publishers began to credit the melody to Carl Mueller, who has not been identified. But as a result, this melody is known as *Mueller*, and is commonly used in the United States. The other version, known as the *Cradle Song*, is more common in the rest of the world.

I'm breaking with the format used elsewhere in this book by placing the discussion of the two versions on facing pages. The music for both versions falls on facing pages, so they can be combined into a medley if desired. The Mueller version is found on page 20.

Performance Tips and Comments
This arrangement is in the key of C, and uses entirely first position chord shapes. The F chord presents the biggest challenge for most people when playing in the key of C. In this arrangement I use two different approaches. In measure 3, I found it easiest to play the F as a barre chord, but do a partial lift of the barre to play the open 2nd string on beat 2. In measure 7, I don't barre, and use my thumb to fret the low F. This makes it easier to move my fingers to facilitate playing melody notes. But you could use either approach in both cases. Another option is to not play the low bass note, and just make the 3rd fret, 4th string the lowest note. That would work for all occurrences of F in this arrangement.

The are several easy chord substitution you could try in this tune. Any C chord that doesn't have the melody note on top could be changed to a Cmaj7 - the opening chord in measure 1, for example. Some of the C chords, measures 2 and 14, for example, sound nice when replaced by Am, as well. Many of the F chords sound good as an Fmaj7.

Introduction Suggestions
For a standard introduction, you could play the final four bars, starting at measure 13, optionally going to a G or G7 at the end to set up the verse. Arpeggios over any basic chord sequence of C, F and G would also work well.

Ending Suggestions
You could repeat the last four bars, starting with the pickup to measure 13, or simply ritard the final few bars.

Sample Recording
The performance on the recording is very simple, with an introduction consisting of some arpeggios over C, F, C, G. I then played the tune as written one time, before repeating with added arpeggios on the longer chords, and some timing variations. I ended with the suggested "tag" ending, ritarding into the final C chord.

AWAY IN A MANGER (CRADLE)

Words: Unkown/Traditional
Music: William J. Kirkpatrick (1895)

The cattle are lowing, the baby awakes,
But little Lord Jesus, no crying he makes.
I love thee, Lord Jesus! look down from the sky,
And stay by my cradle till morning is nigh.

This is the other melody commonly used for *Away in a Manger*. This melody was first published in 1895, under the title *Luther's Cradle Hymn,* with the idea that the words were composed by Martin Luther, and was described as a popular German song. Like many traditional songs, the words may be sung to many different melodies. It is estimated that over 200 different melodies have been used for this song.

The two melodies presented here are compatible, and I arranged them in the same key here, so they could make a nice medley. You might play one after the other, or insert one in the middle of the other. The *Cradle Song* version follows the *Mueller* version on page 21.

Performance Tips and Comments
Like the *Mueller* version, this tune is in the key of C, but has some more interesting harmony, bringing in some minor chords. The melody does reach up to an A, 1st string, 5th fret, but it should be easy to slide up to reach that note. The melody is a little busier than the Mueller melody, but since the tune can be played slowly, there should still be space to add some embellishments as well as alter the phrasing if you wish.

Introduction Suggestions
Any chord progression in C would work as an introduction, even just C to G7, but you might want to introduce some of the minor chords. C, Am, Dm, G7 would be one possible introduction.

Ending Suggestions
You could just ritard into the final few measures, or repeat the last four bars.

Sample Recording
I started the sample recording with a simple progression, consisting of C, C/B, Am7, played twice. You can basically finger the C chord, and walk the bass notes on the 5th string down, C, B, then A. The first verse is played as written, but on the final chord, I repeat the introduction pattern as a short interlude before returning to the melody a second time through. The second time adds arpeggios, and varies the timing and phrasing a little to try to make the song flow. I fattened up the high A on the 1st string, 5th fret in measure 3 by also playing a C on the 3rd string, 5th fret. Upon reaching the end, I again played the C, C/B, Am7 pattern once, leading into a tag ending – starting with the pickup notes to measure 13.

AWAY IN A MANGER (MUELLER)

Traditional
Arr. Doug Young

AWAY IN A MANGER (CRADLE)

Unknown/Kirkpatrick
Arr. Doug Young

BRING A TORCH, JEANETTE, ISABELLA

Words and music: Traditional, 17th Century French

Bring a torch, Jeanette, Isabella!
Bring a torch, to the stable call
Christ is born. Tell the folk of the village
Jesus is born and Mary's calling.
Ah! Ah! beautiful is the Mother!
Ah! Ah! beautiful is her child.

Bring a Torch is a 17th century carol that comes from the Provence region of France. The song tells the story of two women who find a mother and baby in a stable, but was not originally associated with Christmas. The song is often written in 3/8 time, but is shown here in 3/4 time for easier reading.

Performance Tips and Comments

This arrangement should be fairly easy to play, but does move along a bit faster than some. Although the tune is in 3/4 time, I generally count it in "1," thinking of the feel as being more like triplets, tapping my foot once for each measure. My harmonization of the song follows a common I-vi-ii-V chord progression, which is similar to many popular tunes, especially 50's era "doo-wop". Although this tune spans two pages, the more rapid pace means that it is relatively short, so you may want to develop more variations to keep it interesting through repeated verses. However, the faster pace also provides less time to add extra notes.

Introduction Suggestion

A simple 3/4 pattern on C would set up the feel well for this tune. You could also use the I-vi-ii-V chord progression as an introduction.

Ending Suggestions:

The tag ending approach works well for this song. You could even repeat the phrase that starts at bar 24 multiple times.

Sample Recording

For the sample recording, I played an arpeggiated pattern over C, Am7, Dm, G, before playing the tune once as written. The intro was played like this on the recording:

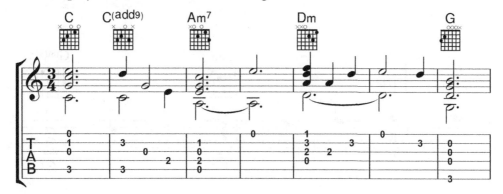

For the second verse, I simply added a few extra bass notes and arpeggiated chord tones where there was room. I ended the song with the tag ending starting at measure 24.

BRING A TORCH, JEANETTE, ISABELLA

French Traditional
Arr. Doug Young

COVENTRY CAROL

Words: Traditional 16th Century English
Music: Thomas Mawdyke (1591)

Lully, lullah, thou little tiny child,
Bye bye, lully, lullay.
Thou little tiny child,
Bye bye, lully, lullay.

This 16th century carol originated in Coventry, England and was performed as part of an annual Christmas pageant. The song refers to the Massacre of the Innocents, in which King Herod ordered the death of all male infants under 2 years old. The melody is hauntingly minor, but ends with a major chord, known as a Picardy third. This technique was common in Renaissance music.

Performance Tips and Comments

This tune fits well in the first position and should be quite easy to play. Focus on playing smoothly and letting notes ring out. The juxtaposition of minor and major chords, both the E in measures 4 and 12, and the A major at the end helps make the minor key more haunting. The chord in measure 11 could be considered a Dm6/F (as written), or a Fmaj#11, and also introduces a unique color. You could play the F bass note on the 6th string, 1st fret, if you'd prefer.

Introduction Suggestions

A simple vamp in 3/4 time, to establish the tempo should work well as an introduction, and many chord sequences are possible. Try Am, Em back and forth a few times, Am, Dm, or Am, G.

Ending Suggestions

The dramatic final A major chord makes such a strong statement, it doesn't seem effective to add anything more to end the piece. Just be sure to let the A ring loud strong and clear.

Sample Recording

On the recording, I used Am, E (major) as an introductory vamp. After playing the song as written, I played it two more times, just adding additional arpeggios where there was space and varying the phrasing a bit. When embellishing, I sometimes played the Am chord as an Am(add9), with the 2nd string open, which adds a pleasantly dissonant character. For an ending, I used a slight variation on the tag ending idea. At measure 14, before hitting the A major, I returned to measure 13, repeating this partial line twice, before finally landing on A major.

COVENTRY CAROL

Traditional/Mawdyke
Arr. Doug Young

GO TELL IT ON THE MOUNTAIN

Words and Music: African-American Spiritual, 1860s

Go tell it on the mountain,
over the hills and everywhere;
go tell it on the mountain,
that Jesus Christ is born.

This African-American spiritual is used as a Christmas song, but has also been recorded by popular music groups, including Peter, Paul, and Mary, who cast it as a civil rights song. The song may have its roots in the spiritual Go Down Moses.

Performance Tips and Comments

This tune has a verse and a chorus, but usually starts with the chorus ("Go Tell It On The Mountain") first. So play it in the order written here, but on the final pass, end on measure 8, at the end of the chorus. The arrangement falls easily in the 1st position, except for measures 4, 9 and 13, where you will need to reach the 1st string, 5th fret. In measure 4, I use my index finger to play the G bass note, and pinky to reach the 5th fret high A. The note at the end of measure 9 goes by faster, and I simply slide up my pinky from the 3rd fret, form the G/B chord and quickly play the note before sliding back down for the next chord shape.

Although the song is fairly simple, the chord changes go by rather quickly, usually changing every two beats. This song may need some practice and attention to changing chords efficiently, especially if you want to play it at faster tempos.

Introduction Suggestion

The chorus is the most recognizable part of the song, so the last phrase, starting at the pickup note to measure 7 could be used as an intro. Any C-based progression, such as C, F, C, G, would work as well.

Ending Suggestions:

Repeating the final two measures, with a ritard, works well for this tune.

Sample Recording

On the recording, I play a fairly free-time introduction based on measures 6 through 8. After playing the chorus and one verse as-written, I go back to the chorus, adding an alternating bass. If you finger the chords as shown, you can simply play quarter notes in the bass, alternating between the bass note shown and the 4th string.

On the second pass through the verse, I just add some bass notes and arpeggiated chord tones occasionally, then return to the alternating bass style for the last time through the chorus. You could maintain the alternating bass style throughout the verse as well. For the ending, I repeated the last line, starting with the pickup note into measure 7 and slowed down as I approached the final chord.

GO TELL IT ON THE MOUNTAIN

Traditional Spiritual
Arr. Doug Young

GOD REST YE MERRY, GENTLEMEN

Words and Music: Traditional 16th Century English

God rest ye merry, gentlemen
Let nothing you dismay
For Jesus Christ, our Saviour
Was born upon this day.

God Rest Ye Merry, Gentlemen is one of the oldest carols still being sung today. The English carol was mentioned in Charles Dicken's *A Christmas Carol*. Wikipedia notes that the phrase "Rest ye merry" has been traced back to the 1540s.

Performance Tips and Comments

The song is in Am, and is mostly based on the Aeolean mode, although Aeolean would use an Em chord, instead of the E major used in this arrangement. You might try replacing the E chords with Em for a different sound.

Introduction Suggestions

Any A minor pattern would work well, Am and E or E7, for example. Am and F creates a more ambiguous and mysterious sound.

Ending Suggestions

The last three measures can be repeated. Another option would be to vamp on Am to F a few times before ending on Am.

Sample Recording

For the example recording, I played an introduction based on the first two chords, but leaving the top strings open on the F chord. Here is what I played on the introduction:

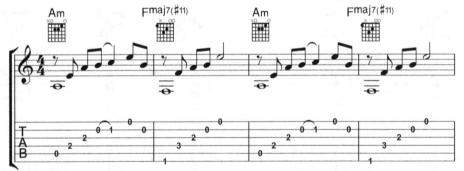

For the ending, I repeated the last phrase, but with a twist. After playing the Am in measure 19, I went to an F (similar to my introduction) before repeating the final phrase and ending on an arpeggiated Am(add9) chord.

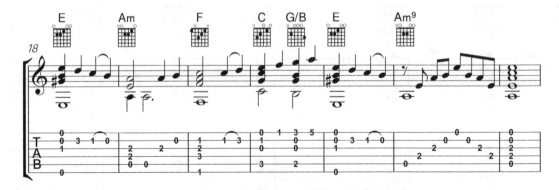

GOD REST YE MERRY, GENTLEMEN

Traditional
Arr. Doug Young

GOOD KING WENCESLAS

Words: John Mason Neale (1853)
Music: Traditional

Good King Wenceslas looked out,
on the Feast of Stephen,
When the snow lay round about,
deep and crisp and even.

Good King Wenceslas is based on a legend about Saint Wensceslas, the Duke of Bohemia. The lyrics, written by Neale, were set to a 13th century carol known as *Tempus Adest Floridum*. The tune has an unusual structure, consisting of 17 bars.

Performance Tips and Comments
Good King Wenceslas is in 4/4 time, in the key of G. This arrangement fits easily in first position, and should present very few challenges. However, the chords change every two beats most of the time. In measure 16, I find it easiest to play a full F barre chord, but you could change fingerings between the two half-notes, or you could play the F bass note with your thumb.

Like many carols and hymns, the song also has a lot of repetition. For example, bars 5-8 are an exact repeat of bars 1-4. Measures 11-12 are the same as measures 3-4 and 7-8. Measure 9 is the same as measure 15. The similarities should help when working out the fingering, and also present opportunities to add variations to keep the song interesting.

Introduction Suggestions
The last four, or the last two measures could be used as an introduction, as well as any common key of C chord progression.

Ending Suggestions
You could end the tune by holding the two half notes in measure 16 twice as long before the final chord. The last phrase, starting at measure 13 makes a good tag ending, or you could repeat just the final two measures, or even the final three.

Sample Recording
For the sample recording, I based in the introduction on the opening four chords with one small change. I played arpeggios over C, G/B, Am, G (playing a G/B instead of C/B). The second time through the song, I added additional chordal tones as arpeggios under the melody and varied the phrasing and timing in a few places. To create an ending, I played the F in measure 16, but then played an Am instead of the final C – creating a "false" ending – before repeating measure 16, and ending on the expected C chord.

GOOD KING WENCESLAS

John Mason Neale
Arr. Doug Young

HARK! THE HERALD ANGELS SING

Words: Charles Wesley and George Whitefield (1739)
Music: Mendolsohn/Cummings

Hark! The herald-angels sing
Glory to the newborn king;
Peace on earth and mercy mild,
God and sinners reconciled.

The lyrics to this song come from a poem, *Hymn for Christmas-Day* by Charles Wesley, with later changes by George Whitefield. William Cummings adapted the melody from a Mendelssohn cantata.

Performance Tips and Comments

Hark! The Herald Angels Sing is in 4/4 time, and this arrangement is in the key of C. There are chord changes every two beats through most of the tune, but they are mostly easy first position chords. There are some opportunities to make simple chord substitutions to create a different sound. For example, Cmaj7 works well for any C chord that doesn't have a C as the top melody note. Measures 3 and 4 are good examples. The F chord in measure 3 could be played as an Am7, for easier fingering. Measures 13 and 17 require a small jump to play the melody note on the 1st string, 5th fret. You could bar the top three strings of the F chord, creating an Fmaj7 chord, although it becomes more challenging to play smoothly.

Introduction Suggestions

The last phrase, measures 19 and 20, could be used as an introduction. In this case, you could either play the final C chord and then go to G7 before starting the melody, or just stop on the G7 chord in measure 20. For example, consider the following idea, which very loosely mimics the last phrase, hinting at the melody without copying it exactly:

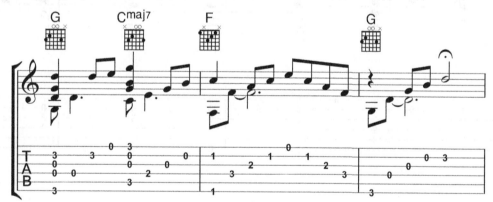

Ending Suggestions

You could just ritard, holding out the notes in the final measure longer for effect. The last two measures makes a good tag ending (as marked), but you could also repeat the final four measures. If you use a tag ending, consider substituting an Am for the C chord in measure 20 before jumping back to repeat the last phrase.

Sample Recording

On the recording, I started with a simple arpeggio pattern over C, before playing the first verse as-written. For the second verse, I added some additional notes, trying to keep a fairly steady flow of arpeggios going under the melody. For an ending, I simply ritard into the final two measures.

HARK! THE HERALD ANGELS SING

Wesley / Whitefield
Arr. Doug Young

HERE WE COME A-WASSAILING

Words and Music: Traditional 19th Century English

Love and joy come to you,
And to you your wassail too;
And God bless you
and send you a Happy New Year
And God send you a Happy New Year.

This 19th century carol refer to "wassailing" or "caroling". A Wassail was a bowl of ale, which the carolers hoped they would be offered by the households they were caroling.

Performance Tips and Comments

This arrangement has some unique challenges. The first part of the tune is in 6/8 time, and has a bouncing rhythm. The chorus shifts into 2/4 time, starting with the pickup notes in measure 7. If you count the 6/8 time in "2", you can basically tap your foot the same way through each part, but the feel is different. The chords, while simple, move very quickly, especially in the chorus, making this tune more challenging to play than many others in this book. Pay close attention to fingerings; I've tried to optimize for minimal movement. For example, the figure in measures 8 and 9, finger the C chord as a Cadd9, which means you simply have to move your finger from the 3rd fret, 6th string, to the 3rd fret 5th string to switch between G and C.

Introduction Suggestions

One option is to set up the 6/8 time with a rhythmic pattern on the G chord.

Ending Suggestions

A tag ending, repeating the section from measure 15 works well, and could even be repeated multiple times.

Sample Recording

I began this performance with a 6/8 rhythm on a G chord, followed by D. After playing once as written, I returned to the same introductory rhythm briefly, then played a second time. This tune moves along so quickly, there's not a lot of room to add more notes, and I just focused on trying to play a little more freely the second time, adding some occasional pull offs and hammer-ons. For the chorus, I took a different approach, and played *less*, focusing on the melody and phrasing. Some melody notes are anticipated, and some bass notes are delayed. This makes the section somewhat easier to play, since I'm not trying to play as many notes squarely on the beat.

For the ending, I first played an Em instead of the G chord in measure 18, before repeating the final phrase from the pickup notes in measure 15. This is a technique that can be used effectively in most songs. The general approach is to substitute the relative minor of the key for the final chord, which produces a surprising twist that feels unresolved. Then resolve the "unfinished" feel by repeating the line and ending on the originally intended chord.

HERE WE COME A-WASSAILING

Traditional
Arr. Doug Young

IN THE BLEAK MIDWINTER

Words: Christina Rossetti (1872)
Music: Gustav Hoist (1906)

In the bleak mid-winter
Frosty wind made moan;
Earth stood hard as iron,
Water like a stone.

In the Bleak Midwinter is based on a poem by Christina Rossetti, later put to music by Gustav Hoist.

Performance Tips and Comments

This beautiful tune lays well in the key of C, but watch for measure 10, where you need to jump up to the 5th fret for the melody note. For a softer, prettier sound, many of the C chords could be replaced with Cmaj7. You could play a Dm7 in measure 9, and the F in measure 10 could also be an Fmaj7 (barre strings 1-3 on the 5th fret). The song is generally played somewhat slowly, which provides space for enhancements.

Introduction Suggestions

Any C-base chord progression would work well for this song. Try a variation on the first two measures: C, G/B, Am, G. Or perhaps C, Cmaj7, F, G.

Ending Suggestions

The suggested introductions could also be used as endings.

Sample Recording

On the example recording, I played arpeggios over C, F, Am, G, before starting the first time though the song. Here's what I played for the introduction:

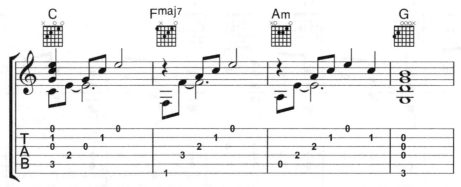

The second time through, I played mostly a series of 8th notes within the chord shapes. The ending simply repeats the last two measures, ritarding slightly to the end.

For an additional example of this tune, I recorded an extended version based on this same arrangement on my CD, *Forever Christmas* – (available Oct 2020) on Spotify or other streaming services, as well as Bandcamp. The CD version adds a cello part and a second guitar, and demonstrates how you can expand a simple arrangement like this into a fuller production.

IN THE BLEAK MIDWINTER

Christina Rossetti / Gustav Hoist
Arr. Doug Young

IT CAME UPON A MIDNIGHT CLEAR

Words: Edmund Sears (1849)
Music: Richard Stoeres Willis (1850)

It came upon the midnight clear,
That glorious song of old,
From angels bending near the earth,
To touch their harps of gold.

It Came Upon a Midnight Clear was written by Edmund Sears, a Unitarian minister. The lyrics focus on "peace on earth", likely because it was written just after the end of the Mexican-American war.

Performance Tips and Comments

This song is in 6/8 time, and I tend to count the beat in "2", with a triplet feel. I play the F chords in tune using my index finger for the bass note (1st fret, 6th string), lifting the bass note as needed to play the melody notes around it. Watch for the E chord in measure 9. I don't finger the 5th string of this chord, making it easier to reach the F# on the 4th string, 4th fret in the melody.

Introduction Suggestions

A simple 6/8 picking pattern on a C chord for a few measures works nicely. Or try C, F, and G.

Ending Suggestions

The final two measures, "to hear the angels sing", can be repeated. I like the effect of playing an Am in measure 16, then jumping back to the pickup note to measure 15 to repeat the phrase, ending on C.

Sample Recording

For the example recording, I played a 6/8 picking pattern over C to G for a simple introduction. The second time through the song, I added some additional bass and arpeggiated notes, although the melody moves fairly fast, and doesn't leave much room for extras. For the ending, I used the approach suggested above, substituting an Am for the C chord in measure 16 before repeating the final phrase. Here's what I played on the recording:

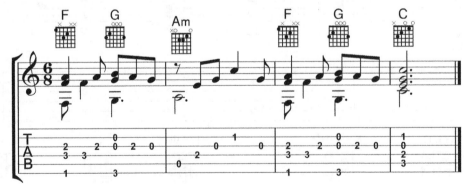

IT CAME UPON A MIDNIGHT CLEAR

Edmund Sears / Richard Willis
Arr. Doug Young

JOY TO THE WORLD

Words: Isaac Watts (1719)
Music: Unknown (1848)

Joy to the world, the Lord is come
Let earth receive her King.

The lyrics to *Joy To The World* are based on Psalm 98. The familiar melody was added much later (1848), in a publication by Lowell Mason. He called the melody "Antioch" and attributed it to Handel.

Performance Tips and Comments

Although this tune is usually played fairly fast, the melody and chords all fall comfortably in first position. For variations, consider adding an alternating bass.

Introduction Suggestions

Try a simple 4/4 picking pattern on G.

Ending Suggestions

You could end by simply ritarding into the final measures, or see below for a more complex approach.

Sample Recording

In the second verse, I included some chord substitutions. In measure 12, instead of staying on G for 2 measures, I played a descending bass line, G, F#, then ending on an Em chord for measure 13, like this:

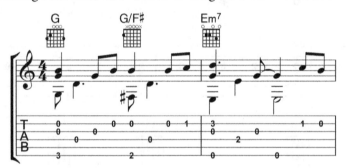

You can often substitute the relative minor for a major chord (for example, Em for G). In measure 14, I used a similar technique, walking down from the D chord, to C, then finally replacing the D7 in measure 15 with an Am. This works in this case because the melody note is a C, which occurs in both the D7 and Am.

Finally, for an ending, I played the final 2 measures three times. The first time, I replaced the G chord in measure 19 with an Em, the relative minor, which sets up a feeling of incompleteness. I also played the D chord as D/F#, so that I had a bass line walking down from G to C. On the second repeat, I replaced the G with a C chord, again creating an unresolved feeling. The third time, I finally ended on a G chord, ending the song. Here's the ending as played on the recording. Notice that it looks quite complicated, but I'm simply thinking of the ending as written, adding picking patterns, the descending bass and the chord substitutions.

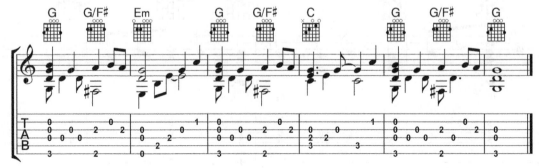

JOY TO THE WORLD

Issac Watts
Arr. Doug Young

O CHRISTMAS TREE

Words: Ernst Anschutz (1824)
Music: Traditional (16th century)

O Christmas tree, o Christmas tree
How lovely are thy branches
O Christmas tree, o Christmas tree
How lovely are thy branches.

Ernst Anschutz based *O Christmas Tree* (also known as *O Tannenbaum*) on an older traditional German song. The song was originally unrelated to Christmas, but grew in popularity as a Christmas song as Christmas trees became common. Tannenbaum literally means "fir tree", and the lyrics have evolved over the years, as people have added more religious and explicitly Christmas lyrics.

Performance Tips and Comments

This song should be easy to play, but it is sometimes played at a fairly fast tempo, which may introduce a few challenges. Of course, if you are playing as an instrumental, you could easily play the song slower, even interpreting it as a slow ballad. One challenging spot is measure 11. If you are able to handle the stretch, you might play the G bass note with your second finger, and the 1st string 1st fret with your first, leaving your ring finger and pinky to play the 3rd fret notes. Another approach is to use your ring and 1st fingers for the initial G7 chord, and play the next note (2rd fret, 2nd string) with your pinky. Then roll your pinky to play the last note, 3rd fret, 1st string.

Measure 9 requires a jump out of first position, but should be fairly easy. You should be playing the C chord at the beginning of the measure with your pinky on the 1st string, so just slide it up to the 5th fret.

Introduction Suggestions

For a very simple introduction, just play a 3/4 picking pattern over a C chord, or C and G.

Ending Suggestions

You could ritard into the last measure, perhaps with a long hold on the G chord at the end of measure 15. Or repeat the final 2 measures as a tag ending.

Sample Recording

I began the sample recording with a 3/4 pattern over C, G/B, Am, G, with the bass descending and the top note moving up from a C to a G. The second time through the tune, I anticipated some bass notes to give the arrangement some sense of motion. The song moves along fairly fast, leaving little time to add embellishments, although I tried to keep the recording at a moderate pace with a gentle feel. In measure 9, I played the Am chord as a partial barre, allowing me to fill in some arpeggiated notes. For the ending, I simply repeated the last two measures, starting with the pickup note to measure 15.

O CHRISTMAS TREE

Ernst Anschutz
Arr. Doug Young

O COME ALL YE FAITHFUL

Words and Music: John Wade (1751)

O come, all ye faithful, joyful and triumphant!
O come ye, O come ye to Bethlehem;
Come and behold him Born the King of Angels:
O come, let us adore Him, Christ the Lord.

The origins of this popular Christmas song are unclear. The song was first published by John Wade in 1751, but may date to as early as the 13th century. Some attribute the song to King John IV of Portugal around 1640.

Performance Tips and Comments

This arrangement is in the key of C, and should be fairly easy, although the chords move somewhat rapidly in the second half of the song. Measure 18 is a slightly awkward spot. The last note of the measure could be played as a Dm chord, but the change would be quite fast. Instead, I play the Am chord with my index, ring finger and pinky, allowing me to play the final note on the 1st fret, 1st string with my index finger.

Introduction Suggestions

The last two measures of the song would make a good introduction. Note that you could play them as written, with the melody, or just hint at the melody by playing arpeggios of C, G, C. The final four measures are another option, as is any 4/4 pattern over chords from the key of C.

Ending Suggestions

Consider repeating either the last four measures, as indicated, or the last two. There are several effective "false endings" you could use to set up the repeat. You could replace the C chord in measure 20 with an Am before repeating the last phrase. An F chord also works well. In both cases, be sure to play the C on the 1st fret, 2nd string to maintain the same melody, but with an unexpected harmony.

Sample Recording

On the example recording I created an introduction by playing C, G/B, Am, G, leading into the first verse. I tried to keep the improvised second pass fairly simple, just adding an additional bass note in each measure during the first 8 bars, before starting to be a bit busier during the second half of the tune.

For the ending, I jumped quickly from the C chord in measure 20 to a G/B, leading back to the pickup notes to measure 17. In measure 18, I played the Am, and followed by a Dm chord, holding it out for effect, before resuming with the final two measures. Here's what I played on the recording, starting with measure 20:

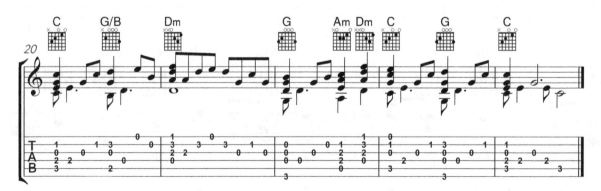

O COME ALL YE FAITHFUL

John Wade
Arr. Doug Young

O COME, O COME, EMMANUEL

Words: Anonymous (1710)
Music: Traditional (1400s)

O come, O come, Emmanuel!
Redeem thy captive Israel
That into exile drear is gone,
Far from the face of God's dear Son.
Rejoice! Rejoice! Emmanuel
Shall come to thee, O Israel.

O Come, O Come, Emmanuel comes from the plainchant tradition. The lyrics first appeared in Latin in 1710, although the song could be much older. It was first published in English in 1861. The melody used today came much later, first appearing in print in 1851. However, some trace the melody to 15th century France.

Performance Tips and Comments

The song is in Am, has a somber feel, and is often performed in fairly free time. Early arrangements often show no time signature at all. I've arranged it in 4/4 time, and made the phrases fit within the structure, but you could easily play the tune more freely. For example, the chord at the end of each phrase, measures 3, 6, and 9 could be held out longer, if you feel like it.

Unlike most songs in this book, this arrangement has an AAB structure, a verse with a first ending in measure 12, a second verse with a second ending and then a chorus.

Introduction Suggestions

Any chord pattern based around the key of Am could work. Am and Em, or Am and Dm would set the song up nicely. I would try to use a lot of open strings, and perhaps some more ambiguous-sounding chords, such as an Am(add9) - created by including the open 2nd string B.

Ending Suggestions

Repeating the final phrase, starting with the pickup to measure 18 works well.

Sample Recording

On the sample recording, I created an introduction by playing an arpeggio pattern over Am, then Em. I repeated Am, then finished with a natural harmonic on the top three strings of the 12th fret (which sounds as Em).

After playing once as written including repeats, I played a second time though the song adding some additional chordal notes and arpeggios where there was room.

For an ending, I repeated the last 4 bars, playing more slowly, and ritarding to the final G chord.

If you'd like to hear how a simple arrangement like this can be built into a fuller production, my CD, *Forever Christmas* (released Oct 2020), includes an expanded version of this song. That recording is based directly on this arrangement - I played the main guitar part exactly as suggested in this book, by reading the music while freely adding minor variations. From that starting point, I added cello, recorder and additional guitars.

O COME, O COME, EMMANUEL

Traditional
Arr. Doug Young

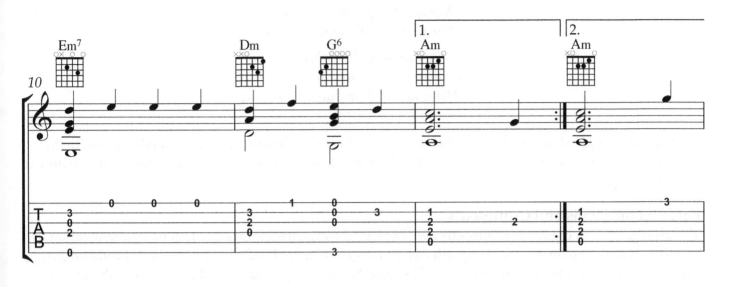

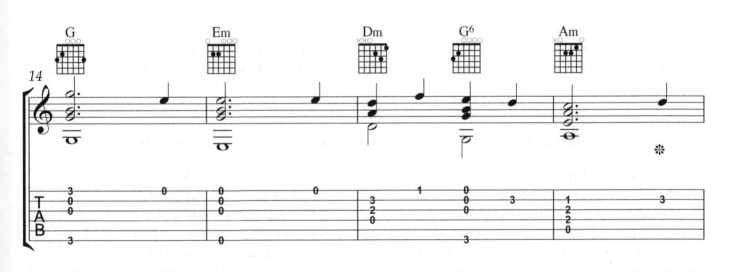

O LITTLE TOWN OF BETHLEHEM

Words: Phillips Brooks (1865)
Music: Lewis Rendner (1868)

O little town of Bethlehem,
How still we see thee lie;
Above thy deep and dreamless sleep
The silent stars go by.

O Little Town of Bethlehem was written by Phillips Brooks for his Sunday School, inspired by a visit to the town of Bethlehem. The music was added at Brooks' request, and was apparently written the evening before it was first performed.

Performance Tips and Comments

This arrangement in the key of C is mostly easy to play. However, the 1st measure requires some attention to be able to play the Eb on the 2nd string, 4th fret. I finger the Cmaj7 chord with my first and second fingers, making it easy to play the Eb with my pinky. The melody reaches up to an A on the 1st string, 5th fret twice. Also watch the fingering of the F chord in measure 11. Fretting only the notes shown makes it easier to play the following melody notes. I lift my first finger off the low F bass note to play the C, third note of the measure.

Introduction Suggestions

The last two measures would work well as an introduction, either ending with the C or going to G7 to lead into the melody. Of course any C-based chord progression in 4/4 time would work as well. Consider C, G/B, Am, G (or G7).

Ending Suggestions

You could simply ritard into the final C chord, or repeat the last two measures as a tag ending.

Sample Recording

On the recording, I played arpeggios over Cmaj7, Dm, G to introduce the song. The second time through, I added arpeggiated chords under the melody, and also varied the timing in a few places. For the ending, I moved from the Cin measutre 16 to an Am, then repeated the final two measures. I ended with a Cmaj7 chord, playing a B on the 3rd string, 4th fret. This is an awkward chord, and the clash between the B and C on the 2nd string would not sound pleasant if played together, but it works well when arpeggiated. This approach allows me to play a prettier Cmaj7 sound while keeping the melody note (C) on top. Here what I played for the ending:

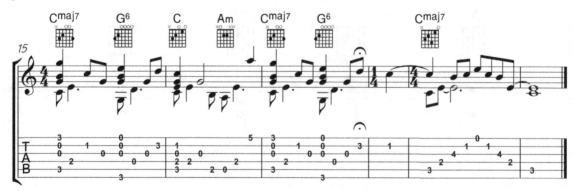

O LITTLE TOWN OF BETHLEHEM

Brooks / Redner
Arr. Doug Young

SILENT NIGHT

Words: Joseph Mohr (1818)
Music: Franz Gruber (1818)

Silent night! Holy night!
All is calm, all is bright
Round yon virgin mother and child!
Holy infant, so tender and mild,
Sleep in heavenly peace!
Sleep in heavenly peace!

Silent Night is one of the best-known Christmas carols, and has the distinction of having been first performed on guitar. Mohr was a priest in Austria, whose church organ had been damaged by a flood. He wrote the lyrics, and asked Franz Gruber to compose the music, using the guitar in place of the damaged organ.

Performance Tips and Comments

Silent Night is fairly straightforward, but placing it in the key of G means that there are a few high notes requiring a jump up to 5th and 7th positions. In measures 17 and 18, I suggest holding a partial barre over the 1st three strings for the D chord. Then just slide your hand, keeping more or less the same position, up three frets to barre at the 5th fret. You only need to change the finger on the 2nd string to adjust for the D7 chord in measure 18.

The other jump occurs in measure 19. I play the G in measure 18 using my pinky on the 1st string. You can slide on the first string (silently, or audibly), while bringing your other fingers into position to play the G /D chord in measure 19. Notice that this chord shape is the same as a first-position D chord, so it should be comfortable and familiar.

There are a few other spots where you may want to play extra attention to fingering in order to play smoothly. I play the D chord in measure 5 using a partial barre at the 2nd fret, while reaching up to the play the high A with my pinky. Then you can simply lift your picky for the D in measure 6. In measure 21, I play the G chord with my index finger on the bass note, and picky on the first string, allowing me to play the next note on the 2nd string with my ring finger.

Introduction Suggestions

You could set up the feel of this song with a simple 3/4 time pattern over G. With tunes in the key of G, the harmonics on the 12th fret, 2nd, 3rd, and 4th strings outline a G major chord, while the harmonics on the 7th fret, same 3 strings form a D chord, which provide some opportunities for interesting introductions.

Ending Suggestions

One way to create an interesting ending to a song is to create a slight detour. For example, in Silent Night, you might try replacing the final G chord with an Em for one measure, then continue with Am, C and finally G. Virtually any chord sequence that uses chords from the key of G can work. Try replacing the G with C, and playing C, G/B, D7, G.

Sample Recording

My recording of Silent Night begins with a 3/4 arpeggio pattern over G, Em, G, and D. After playing once as written, I repeated with a mostly continuous 8th-note picking pattern. For the ending, I continued an 8th note picking pattern on the G in measures 23 and 24, before repeating the last phrase beginning at measure 21. I slowed down on this final phrase, ritarding into the final chord before resuming an 8th note pattern on G for several measures before stopping.

SILENT NIGHT

Franz Gruber
Arr. Doug Young

THE FIRST NOEL

Words: Traditional English

The first Noel the angel did say
Was to certain poor shepherds in fields as they lay;
In fields where they lay, keeping their sheep,
On a cold winter's night that was so deep.

The First Noel is a Cornish song, first published in 1823, but likely dating from the 16th century, or possibly even earlier.

Performance Tips and Comments

This is a pretty tune that works well in the key of G. The chords change with every measure, but should not be too difficult, as they lay well in the first position. I don't finger the entire G chord in measure 1. I simply play the bass note with my ring finger, leaving fingers 1 and 2 free to play the melody line.

Introduction Suggestions

You could play the last four measures as an introduction, or use the chord progression as raw material to create your own introduction that hints at the tune. One option would be to play measures 22-24, pausing on the Dsus chord before starting the melody.

Ending Suggestions

One idea I experimented with on this tune is to hold out the Dsus chord in measure 24 for at least 3 full beats, before slowly playing the final three melody notes. Here's another idea - after the final measure, repeat the last two measures, but play them an octave lower, starting with a C chord:

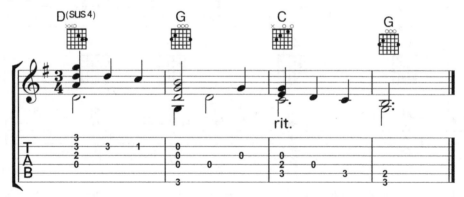

Sample Recording

For the sample recording, I created an introduction by playing a descending bass line over G, G/F#, Em, and then D, ending with harmonics on the 3rd and 2nd strings, 7th fret, which are part of a D chord. On the second time through the song, I varied the timing in places, and also tried to use delayed bass notes. For example, in measure 1, I play the melody note and then the low bass note, followed by an arpeggio that leads into the remainder of the melody. The ending jumps back to repeat the last line, starting at measure 22. I harmonized the last two notes of measure 24 as thirds before ending on the C chord.

THE FIRST NOEL

Traditional
Arr. Doug Young

THE HOLLY AND THE IVY

Words and Music: Traditional British

The holly bears a prickle,
As sharp as any thorn,
And Mary bore sweet Jesus Christ
On Christmas Day in the morn.

This carol first appeared in print was in 1823, but is likely to be much older. The melody first appeared in print in 1911.

Performance Tips and Comments

This tune is remarkably short, creating a challenge when played instrumentally without the benefit of different words for each verse. As written here, the song is 16 measures long but the first eight and last eight bars are nearly identical. However, because the melody is repetitive, you may have more freedom to introduce variations while still keeping the spirit of the song. For example, consider this variation on the first line, which anticipates some melody notes and replaces others with delayed bass notes. The melody has been altered substantially, but should still be recognizable within the context of the song.

Another way to extend a very short song like this is to play interludes between the verses. You could just play the chords without the melody, improvising over picking patterns, or play a short chord pattern like G, G/F#, Em one or more times between verses.

Introduction Suggestions

You could play a chord pattern in 3/4 time using the descending bass line of the first four measures.

Ending Suggestions

The last four measures or just the last two measures make a good repeated ending.

Sample Recording

On the example recording, I created an intro by playing G and D arpeggios as harmonics on the 12th and 5th frets, like this:

After playing as written once, I played the song a second time, adding a few notes where I could and playing a bit more freely. For an ending, I repeated the last four measures, starting with the pickup notes in measure 12, ritarding into the final G chord, ending with a harmonic on strings 4, 3, and 2 at the 5th fret.

THE HOLLY AND THE IVY

Traditional
Arr. Doug Young

61

UP ON THE HOUSETOP

Words and Music: Benjamin Hanby (1864)

Up on the housetop reindeer pause
Out jumps good old Santa Claus.
Down through the chimney, with lots of toys,
All for the little ones Christmas joys.

This is one of the oldest secular Christmas tunes that remains popular today, and was inspired by Clement C Moore's poem *A Visit from St Nicholas*.

Performance Tips and Comments

This tune is straightforward, using only G, C and D chords in the key of G. It would lend itself well to an alternating bass style, with bass notes on every beat, but I've written it with simple bass notes on beats 1 and 3 for easier reading. To add an alternating bass, just play the 4th or 5th strings on beats 2 and 4 while holding the chord shapes. Usually considered a children's song, the tune is usually played fairly fast, with a lively feel.

Introduction Suggestions

The simplest introduction for this tune would be just an alternating bass picking pattern on a G chord for a few measures.

Ending Suggestions

You might repeat the last four measures, or just the last two as an ending. You could also play the final measure in half time, holding out each of the notes in the measure at least two beats.

Sample Recording

The sample recording does not use any introduction. The second time through the song, I moved to an alternating bass style, as described above. For the ending, I repeated the last phrase, starting with measure 13, but held out the last beat of measure 14 for a bit before playing the final two measures up to tempo.

UP ON THE HOUSETOP

Benjamin Hanby
Arr. Doug Young

WE THREE KINGS

Words and Music: John Henry Hopkins (1857)

We Three Kings of Orient are,
Bearing gifts we traverse afar,
Field and fountain,
Moor and mountain,
Following yonder Star.

We Three Kings was one of the first Christmas carols written in the United States to become popular. The song was written for a Christmas pageant in New York City, and was designed for three male singers, acting as each of the Magi.

Performance Tips and Comments

We Three Kings is in 3/4 time in the key of Am. It should be fairly easy to play. It's interesting to notice that it's possible to play the entire first eight measures without lifting your middle finger off the 4th string, 3nd fret. Although the chords show a full Em for some measures, the 5th string is not really needed. It's an opportunity to practice economy of motion.

Watch for the E augmented chord in measure 14. I play that with a partial barre across the 1st fret.

If you'd like to add a little more harmonic interest, you might play measures 18 and 22 as a C/B instead of a straight C chord.

Introduction Suggestions

A picking pattern over Am makes a good intro. You could also play Am and Em back and forth a few times. Consider going to an E augmented chord to lead into the first verse.

Ending Suggestions

The final four measures are fairly dramatic, and can be repeated for an effective ending.

Sample Recording

The sample recording starts with a variation of an idea that's also discussed in *What Child Is This?*, a pattern that starts on an Am(add9) chord on the 5th fret, with a descending line on the fourth string, ending on an E chord. Here's what I played on the recording:

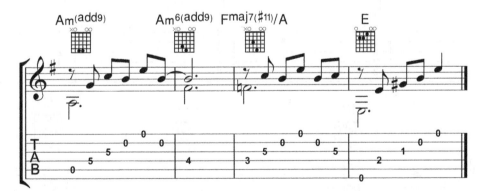

After playing the second time though with some minor variations, I ended the recording by repeating the final four measures, ritarding into the final chord.

WE THREE KINGS

John Hopkins Jr
Arr. Doug Young

WE WISH YOU A MERRY CHRISTMAS

Words and Music: Traditional English

We wish you a merry Christmas
We wish you a merry Christmas
We wish you a merry Christmas
And a happy new year.

The origins of this carol are unclear, but it seems to date from the 1800's in England.

Performance Tips and Comments

This arrangement should be fairly easy, although the pace is usually rather fast. All the chords lie comfortably in the 1st position. I play the F chord by using my thumb to fret the 6th string bass note, but you could use a barre chord, or leave out the 6th string bass, and just play the bass note an octave higher on the 4th string. There is not a lot of room in this song for variations, since it moves so fast. Experimenting with bass notes is probably the easiest enhancement. You could play bass notes on beats 1 and 2, creating a more "oomp-pah" feel, or explore walking bass notes that connect the chords. For example, here's one walking bass approach:

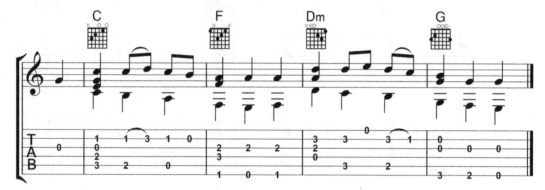

You could also introduce some chord substitutions to create some variety. For example, consider replacing the C to G in measures 9 and 10 with Am and Em.

Introduction Suggestions

A 3/4 pattern, like bass, strum, strum over C or over a descending bass line, C, B, A, G would make a useful introduction.

Ending Suggestions

Repeating either the final four measures, or the final two measures would work as an ending.

Sample Recording

I kept the sample recording very simple; there's no introduction, and on the second time through, I mostly just added an second bass note on the 2nd beat. To end the song, I jumped back to the last phrase, starting with the pickup note to measure 13, slowing down to the final C chord.

WE WISH YOU A MERRY CHRISTMAS

Traditional
Arr. Doug Young

WHAT CHILD IS THIS?

Words: William Chatterton Dix (1865)
Music: Traditional (Greensleeves)

What Child is this, who, laid to rest,
On Mary's lap is sleeping?
Whom angels greet with anthems sweet,
While shepherds watch are keeping?

The lyrics to this popular song were written by Dix in 1865 as a poem, *The Manger Throne*. The melody is the English traditional tune, *Greensleeves*, which dates to at least the 1500's. The tune is mentioned in Shakespeare's play *The Merry Wives of Windsor*. *Greensleeves* is sometimes credited to King Henry the VIII, although it seems unlikely he was the author.

Performance Tips and Comments

The song is in 3/4 time in the key of Am. One part you may find awkward is the E chord in measure 14 and again in measure 30, where the melody dips down to an F# on the 4th string, 4th fret. I finger that chord with my index and middle fingers, skipping the 5th string, which makes it easier to reach the F# with my pinky.

There are a number of simple chord substitutions you can use to introduce some variety. You could move to a C in measures 2 and 10, instead of staying on an Am. In measures 18 and 26, you could play an Am instead of staying on C for two measures. Try reversing the chords in measures 19 and 20, playing Em and then G (while keeping the melody the same, of course). You could substitute an F for the Am in measure 21 or measure 29. Also, this tune is sometimes played with a melodic change, using an F# (2nd fret, 1st string) as the 2nd note of measure 2 instead of the F natural. This has the effect of changing the mode of the tune from Aeolean to Dorian minor.

Introduction Suggestions

The are endless possibilities for introductions to fairly slow minor tunes in Am. Here's an example of an interesting chord progression you can try. It starts with an Am(add9) chord at the 5th fret, and then lowers the note on the 4th string to and F# and then an F, before ending on an E. You can play various rhythm patterns over this progression.

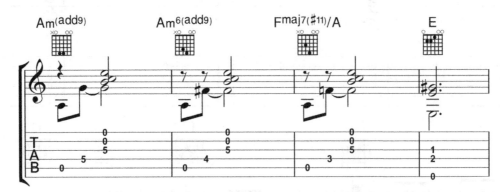

Ending Suggestions

One option for an ending would be to reuse the previous introduction idea, resolving to a final Am chord. You could just ritard and end on the Am chord, or consider jumping up to the Am(add9) on the 5th fret for the final chord. Another idea is to use the false ending approach – in this case, replace the Am in measure 31 with an F major chord before repeating the last phrase.

Sample Recording

I started the sample recording with a simple Am, E, Am, E introduction. In the second verse, I took some liberties with timing, but mostly tried to add additional chordal tones and arpeggios beneath the melody. For the ending, I repeated the last line, starting with the pickup notes to measure 19, then ending by playing an Am in first position, jumping up to an Am9 in the 5th position (fretting the 3rd and 4th strings on the 5th).

Like several other arrangements in this book, *What Child is This?* is included in my CD, *Forever Christmas* (released Oct 2020). I asked a friend to join me on recorder for that version, but the guitar part is based directly on this arrangement - I played the main guitar part as suggested in this book, by reading the music while freely adding minor variations.

WHAT CHILD IS THIS?

Traditional
Arr. Doug Young

ABOUT THE AUTHOR

Doug Young is fingerstyle guitarist, composer, performer and author who lives in the San Francisco Bay Area. He is a Contributing Editor to Acoustic Guitar Magazine and the author of the best-selling Mel Bay book, *Understanding DADGAD for Fingerstyle Guitar* as well as *Fiddle Tunes for DADGAD, A DADGAD Christmas* and *Acoustic Guitar Amplification Essentials* (String Letter Publishing). He has released multiple CDs of original music and arrangements, *Laurel Mill* and *Closing Time,* which are available with accompanying transcriptions, *DUETS,* a collection of fingerstyle duets with Teja Gerken, and *Forever Christmas,* arrangements of instrumental Christmas music featuring acoustic guitar as well as violin, viola, cello and recorder/flute.

This book is part of a series. Volume 1, *Hymns for Fingerstyle Guitar,* and Volume 3, *More Hymns for Fingerstyle Guitar,* follow the same philosophy and approach, providing more songs and arrangements.

For comments or questions about this book, contact the author at:
doug@dougyoungguitar.com

Books are available through Amazon.com and MelBay.com. CDs and tablature are available from the author's website:
http://www.dougyoungguitar.com

OTHER BOOKS BY DOUG YOUNG
AVAILABLE ON AMAZON.COM

Hymns for Fingerstyle Guitar is the first volume in the Fingerstyle Fakebook Series. The book follows the same style and format as this book, and contains twenty-five classic hymns, arranged for guitar in standard tuning.

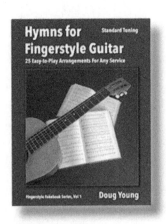

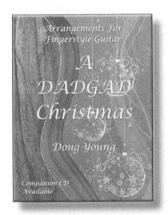

A DADGAD Christmas offers a collection of Christmas Carols arranged for solo instrumental guitar in DADGAD tuning. The book is split into two sections. The first follows a similar format to this book - easy to play, single-page arrangements that you can sight-read and use as the basis of improvised elaborations. The second part of the book provides full-length fingerstyle arrangements in DADGAD tuning.

MORE Hymns for Fingerstyle Guitar is the third volume in the Fingerstyle Fakebook Series. The book follows the same style and format as this book, and contains twenty-five additional classic hymns, arranged for solo fingerstyle guitar in standard tuning.

Understanding DADGAD is an instructional book designed to introduce this popular alternate tuning. The book starts from the beginning, progressing through chords, scales, melodic exercises and more. Two hundred examples provide a solid foundation for you to explore this tuning and create your own arrangements.

Made in the USA
Las Vegas, NV
23 November 2024

12479275R00044